What's Christmas?

Text copyright © Alexa Tewkesbury 2006

Illustrations copyright © CWR 2006

Published 2006 by CWR, Waverley Abbey House, Waverley Lane, Farnham, Surrey, GU9 8EP, England.
This reformatted edition published 2011 by CWR.

The right of Alexa Tewkesbury to be identified as the author of this work has been asserted by her in
accordance with the Copyright, Designs and Patents Act 1988.

Concept development, editing, design and production by CWR.

Illustrated by Steve Boulter.

Printed in the UK by Bishops Printers

ISBN: 978-1-85345-612-1

National Distributors include

UK: (and countries not listed below) CWR, Waverley Abbey House, Waverley Lane, Farnham, Surrey GU9 8EP.
Tel: (01252) 784700 Outside UK (44) 1252 784700 Email: mail@cwr.org.uk

AUSTRALIA: KI Entertainment, Unit 21 317-321 Woodpark Road, Smithfield, New South Wales 2164. Tel: 1 800 850 777 Fax: 02 9604 3699 Email: sales@kientertainment.com.au

CANADA: David C Cook Distribution Canada, PO Box 98, 55 Woodslee Avenue, Paris, Ontario N3L 3E5. Tel: 1800 263 2664 Email: sandi.swanson@davidccook.ca

MALAYSIA: Canaanland, No. 25 Jalan PJU 1A/41B, NZX Commercial Centre, Ara Jaya, 47301 Petaling Jaya, Selangor.
Tel: (03) 7885 0540/1/2 Fax: (03) 7885 0545 Email: info@canaanland.com.my

Salvation Book Centre (M) Sdn Bhd, 23 Jalan SS 2/64, 47300 Petaling Jaya, Selangor. Tel: (03) 78766411/78766797 Fax: (03) 78757066/78756360 Email: info@salvationbookcentre.com

NEW ZEALAND: KI Entertainment, Unit 21 317-321 Woodpark Road, Smithfield, New South Wales 2164, Australia.
Tel: 0 800 850 777 Fax: +612 9604 3699 Email: sales@kientertainment.com.au

SINGAPORE: Alby Commercial Enterprises Pte Ltd, 95 Kallang Avenue #04-00, AIS Industrial Building, 339420.
Tel: (65) 629 27238 Fax: (65) 629 27235 Email: marketing@alby.com.sg

SOUTH AFRICA: Struik Christian Books, 80 MacKenzie Street, PO Box 1144, Cape Town 8000. Tel: (021) 462 4360 Fax: (021) 461 3612 Email: info@struikchristianmedia.co.za

Visit www.cwr.org.uk/distributors for full list of National Distributors
CWR is a Registered Charity – Number 294387. CWR is a Limited Company registered in England – Registration Number 1990308

What's Christmas?

by Alexa Tewkesbury

Illustrations by Steve Boulter

CWR

It was daylight. Snow Bear stretched and yawned and poked her small black nose out of her den. Old Polar was already up.

'What are you doing, Old Polar?' asked Snow Bear.

'I was just thinking,' Old Polar replied.

'Thinking what?' queried Snow Bear.

'I was just thinking,' answered Old Polar, 'that it must be nearly Christmas.'

'Christmas?' Snow Bear looked puzzled. 'What's Christmas?'

Old Polar's dark eyes twinkled in his white fur like two glass beads.

'Don't you know?' he mused. 'Then it's time you found out, Snow Bear.' And he ambled away.

Snow Bear sat down and her small black nose
twitched in the freezing air.

There was a sudden explosion of snow in front of her.
An arctic hare shot past in a flurry of white.

'Excuse me,' Snow Bear called, and the flurry
skidded to a halt.
'Are you talking to me?' the hare asked crisply.

'Yes,' answered Snow Bear, lolloping over. 'Can you tell me, please – what's Christmas?'

The hare's whiskers quivered in the pale morning light. 'Don't you know?' he replied. 'Christmas is a girl called Mary riding on a donkey to a town far away, with a very special present.'

Snow Bear frowned.
'What's that supposed to mean?'
'It means what it says,' declared the hare and,
with a flip and a scurry, he was gone.

Snow Bear padded thoughtfully across the winter plains until she came to the cold, calm ocean. The brownish blob of a walrus bobbed up to the surface.

'Hello, Snow Bear,' greeted the blob. 'Want to play?'

'I can't today,' Snow Bear replied. 'I'm trying to find out something very important. Can *you* tell me – what's Christmas?'

The walrus's tusks gleamed against the ice-blue sea.

'Don't you know?' she remarked. 'Christmas is nowhere to stay, just a damp, dingy stable where a tiny new baby lies sleeping in the straw.'

Snow Bear's face fell.

'But that doesn't make sense,' she complained.

'It will,' assured the walrus and,
with a flop and a splash,
she swam away.

Snow Bear trudged slowly along by the water's edge.
Something brightly coloured caught her eye. A puffin was
watching her curiously.
'Can I help you?' the puffin enquired.
'I shouldn't think so,' mumbled Snow Bear.
'Please let me try,' he persisted.

Snow Bear sighed. 'It's just that I'm trying to understand –
what's Christmas?'
The puffin's beak shone like a jewel under the paper-white sky.
'Don't you know?' he chuckled. 'Christmas is a sky full of
angels cheering and singing, and shepherds on a hillside
setting off to meet a King.'
Snow Bear shook her head impatiently.
'But that doesn't mean anything,' she moaned.
'There *must* be something more.'

'Oh, there is,'
smiled the puffin.
'Something much more.'
And, with a flap and a flutter, he flew away.

Snow Bear's small black nose felt cold and damp.
'It's no good,' she muttered, 'I'll never understand Christmas,'
and she plonked herself down on the frozen ground.

'Christmas?' chirped a cheery voice.
'What do you want to know?'

A boy stood in front of her, his shiny, round
face peering out through a muffle of fur.
Snow Bear blinked in the frost-sharp air.

'Well,' she began, 'I know there was Mary and a donkey and a very special present.

I know there was nowhere to stay and a baby in a stable.

I even know there were angels, and some shepherds who went to meet a King. But what I *don't* know is –

What's Christmas?'

The boy smiled. 'But, Snow Bear, that *is* Christmas,' and he sat down beside her and told her how Mary had ridden the donkey to a faraway town called Bethlehem, and how the present was her baby, born in a stable one starry night because there was nowhere for them to stay. He told her how angels had filled the skies over the hilltops, calling the shepherds to go and visit the King, and how the King was the newborn baby, lying sleeping in the straw.

Snow Bear's eyes glistened and her small black nose trembled
with excitement.
'Then I've got it!' she cried. 'Christmas is the King's birthday!'

'Don't you want to know His name?' asked the boy
as Snow Bear turned to gallop home.
'What is it?' she called.
'Jesus!' the boy announced. 'The baby King's
called Jesus!'

Snow Bear raced away and when she found Old Polar,
she tumbled against his soft white tummy and laughed,
'I know! I know!'

'What do you know, Snow Bear?' asked Old Polar, wrapping her up in his great shaggy paws.

'I know what Christmas is,' Snow Bear beamed. 'It's the King's birthday.'

'Well done,' said Old Polar. 'And do you know what Christmas is most of all?'

'You mean there's more?' Snow Bear gasped.

'Much more,' replied Old Polar. 'Most of all, Christmas is love. God's love. The baby King is His Son, and God loves everyone so much that He gave them His very own baby to bring peace and happiness to the whole world.'

'Wow!' murmured Snow Bear, wrinkling her small black nose in amazement. 'God must love everybody a huge amount.' 'Oh, yes,' Old Polar nodded. 'Indeed He does.'